AESOP'S FABLES

Town Mouse and Country Mouse

Adapted by Ronne Randall
Illustrated by Louise Gardner

p

Once there was a roly-poly,
wiggly-whiskered mouse, who
lived in a snug little nest under
an oak tree.

Welcome

Country Mouse loved his home.
He had plenty of acorns, nuts and
berries to eat and a warm and cozy
straw bed to sleep in.

Squirrel and Robin, who lived in
the oak tree, were the best neighbors
he could ever wish for.

One day, Country Mouse had a surprise. His cousin, Town Mouse, came to visit from the Big City.

Town Mouse was sleek and slender, with a smooth, shiny coat. His whiskers were fancy and elegant.

Country Mouse felt a little
ordinary beside him. But he didn't
mind. All he wanted to do was
make Town Mouse feel welcome.

"Are you hungry, Cousin?" he said.
"Come and have some supper!"

But Town Mouse didn't like the
acorns and blackberries that
Country Mouse gave him to eat.
They were tough and sour.

Home
Sweet
Home

And Town Mouse thought
his cousin's friends were boring.

The straw bed that he slept in
that night was so rough and scratchy
that he didn't sleep a wink!

Next day, Town Mouse said, "Come to the Big City with me, Cousin. It's so much more exciting than the country! I live in a grand house, eat delicious food and have exciting adventures. Come with me and see what you've been missing!"

It sounded so wonderful, Country Mouse couldn't resist it. Saying goodbye to his friends, the cousins set off for the city.

When they arrived in the Big City, Country Mouse was frightened. It was *so* noisy—horns blared and wheels clattered all around them. Huge trucks roared and rumbled down the street and the smelly, smoky air made them choke and cough.

And there were dogs *everywhere*!

At last, they arrived safely
at Town Mouse's house.

It was very grand, just as
Town Mouse had said. But
it was *so* big!

Country Mouse was afraid
that he would get lost!

"Don't worry," said Town Mouse to Country Mouse. "You'll soon learn your way around the house. For now, just stay close to me. I'm starving—let's go and have a snack."

Country Mouse was hungry, too, so
he followed his cousin to the kitchen.

Country Mouse had never seen so much delicious food—there were plates full of fruit, nuts, cheese, and cakes.

He and his cousin ate and ate and ate!

But Country Mouse wasn't used to this sort of rich food. Before he knew it, his tummy was aching.

Suddenly, a huge woman came into the room.
"Eek! Mice!" she screamed.

She grabbed a big broom and began to swat the mice, who scampered off as fast as they could.

As the two mice scurried across the
floor, Country Mouse thought
things couldn't possibly get worse.
But how wrong he was!

A big cat suddenly sprang out from
behind a chair! With a loud

M-E-E-O-O-W-W,

he pounced on the two little mice.

Country Mouse had never been so frightened. He darted and dashed as fast as his aching tummy would let him.

The two mice jumped through a mousehole and were safe at last in Town Mouse's house.

"Phew! I think we've done enough for one day," said Town Mouse, when they had caught their breath.

"Let's get some sleep," he said, with a yawn. "I'll show you the rest of the house in the morning."

Country Mouse curled up in the hard little bed. But he was too frightened and unhappy to sleep. As he listened to his cousin snore, he tried hard not to cry.

Next morning, Town Mouse was ready for more adventures, but Country Mouse had had more than enough.

"Thank you for inviting me," he told his cousin, "but I have seen all I want to see of the Big City. It is too big and noisy and dirty—and too full of danger for me. I want to go back to my quiet, peaceful home in the country."

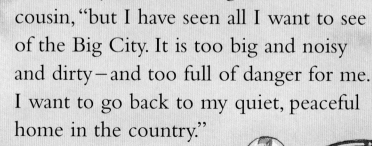

So, Country Mouse went back to his snug, cozy home under the oak tree. He had never been so happy to see his friends – and they wanted to hear all about his adventures.

Country Mouse was pleased to tell them everything that had happened in the Big City – but he *never, ever* went back there again!

COSTUMES AND CLOTHES

Uniforms

Miriam Moss

MARSHALL CAVENDISH
New York . London . Toronto . Sydney

VCA RS WKWC

Reference Edition Published 1989

Published by Marshall Cavendish Corporation
147 West Merrick Road
Freeport, Long Island
N.Y. 11520

©Marshall Cavendish Limited 1989
©Wayland Publishing Ltd 1988

Editor: Deborah Elliott

Reference edition produced by DPM Services Limited

Consultant Editor: Maggi McCormick
Art Editor: Graham Beehag

Printed in Italy by G. Canale C.S.p.A., Turin
Bound in Italy by L.E.G.O. S.p.A., Vicenza

Library of Congress Cataloging-in-Publication Data

Moss, Miriam.
      Uniforms / Miriam Moss.
        p. cm. – (Costumes and Clothes)
      Bibliography: p.
      Includes index.
      Summary: Examines the background and history of
uniforms both military and civilian, including religious,
medical, and sports uniforms.
      ISBN 0-86307-983-0
      ISBN 0-86307-980-6 (Set)
      1. Uniforms–Juvenile literature. [1. Uniforms.] I. Title.
II. Series: Moss, Miriam. Costumes and clothes.
GT1900.M67 1989
391–dc19   88-29281
                                                          CIP
                                                          AC

_10.99_

Contents

What Are Uniforms?

Belonging to a group

The word uniform means "one" or the same form; in other words "alike." When people deliberately wear clothes of the same shape or color, they are wearing uniforms. We think of uniforms as clothes worn by soldiers, nurses, or members of the police force, but there are many other uniforms worn for many different reasons.

Human beings enjoy spending time with each other, and many belong to all sorts of different groups. People in the same group often wear the same color, type, or style of clothing.

Athletes at the opening ceremony of the Olympic Games wear uniforms to show which country they represent. The badges, hats, and scarves worn by soccer fans are all part of their uniform.

This colorful display of uniforms in the Trooping the Colour ceremony outside Buckingham Palace shows that the soldiers all belong to the same group.

The uniforms worn by these Australian rules football players show which team they belong to.

Below These medical scientists are wearing protective uniforms of coveralls, masks, and gloves because they are handling dangerous chemicals.

Uniforms are also used to protect ordinary clothes. Today, laboratory technicians wear white coats and airport maintenance workers wear colored overalls.

Uniforms worn by members of the armed forces are a sign that soldiers, sailors, and airmen and women have a common aim and hold different ranks of importance. They are also a sign of comradeship between service people. The stylish uniforms worn by airline pilots make them seem important because they look like officers in the air force.

Other uniforms show that people have special duties to perform, like policemen and women and nurses. Some uniforms mark people out as having a special style. Often, historical uniforms are used in official ceremonies to give those wearing them a feeling of importance and of being a part of history.

Fighting Uniforms

Infantry uniforms

Infantry soldiers are soldiers who fight on foot. At first, soldiers wore the most practical clothes they had, like tunics. It was very important that soldiers were able to move about freely in hand-to-hand battles, so little **armor** was worn. Helmets and shields were used for protection, and soldiers fought with spears and swords. In time, soldiers started to wear some body armor, like the full-length **greaves** worn by the Spartan Hoplite 2,500 years ago.

In medieval Japan, the infantrymen were called ashigaru. They wore raincapes made from rice straw. The Samurai were Japanese warrior nobles. They wore body armor and carried two razor-sharp swords in their colored sashes.

The helmet, shield, and greaves worn by a Spartan Hoplite.

Japanese Samurai warriors looked very frightening in their body armor.

What differences can you see between these nineteenth-century uniforms, worn by the British infantryman (left), the grenadier guard (center), and the light horseman (right).

Between 1804 and 1815, France, under their leader Napoleon Bonaparté, took on nearly the whole of Europe in battle. Thousands of soldiers were involved in the fighting, and so thousands of uniforms had to be made. The French wore mostly blue, the Russians green, the Austrians white, and the British red. Breeches of white, a dull yellowish-brown, blue, or grey were worn with tall **shakos** and boots made of felt and black leather. Each regiment wore different colored collars, cuffs, and lapels. The uniforms had badges and decorations like colored **plumes**, tassels, and cords, which showed the regiment's history and traditions. The officers' uniforms were trimmed with gold and silver **braid**. The uniforms were brightly colored because it was important that the soldiers could be seen and identified.

A soldier from the Duke of Wellington's army, wearing white pants and a red jacket with blue cuffs and collar.

Cavalry uniforms

The cavalry is the part of the army that is made up of mounted troops (soldiers on horseback). In the thirteenth century, a Mongol cavalry soldier wore almost complete armor. He had a **conical** helmet with a socket for a plume and a brow ridge, chain mail, and a **hauberk** of armor. Greek chariot warriors wore body armor (cuirasses) made of different pieces of bronze and sometimes lined with leather. The helmets are believed to have been made of boars' tusks! They were lined with felt and had an inner cap made of leather thongs with pieces of boars' tusks on top.

Complete armor provided good protection on horseback, but it did mean that the soldiers wearing it were not very **agile** if they were knocked off their horses. The warring knights of the **Middle Ages** wore a uniform of heavy armor. Flags and decorated shields identified them, as there was no other kind of uniform worn and their armor hid their faces.

Above **A dramatic painting of an early nineteenth-century French imperial guard officer.**

An English knight of the Middle Ages, wearing full body armor. No part of his body has been left unprotected.

Although full body armor gradually disappeared with the introduction of fast, accurate guns, cavalry officers in the seventeenth century did sometimes use metal breastplates to protect them in **saber** fighting. Their uniforms were very **ornate**. A French cavalry officer in the 3rd Hussars wore a gray or navy jacket with red braid across his chest, breeches tucked into high boots with spurs, and a dolman — an embroidered jacket worn over one shoulder like a cape, with the sleeves hanging loose.

During the Civil War (1861-65), the Union forces of the north wore dark blue uniforms, while the opposing Confederate troops wore gray jackets and pants. For both, officers were identified by red or yellow piping on their pants.

Uniforms enable soldiers to recognize the enemy in the heat of the battle. This picture shows a Union (right) and a Confederate soldier fighting during the Civil War.

Changing uniforms and World War I

In the nineteenth century when **cartridges** and rifles were introduced, firearms became much more accurate. Toward the end of the century, uniforms became less colorful, as bright uniforms were easy targets to hit from a long distance away. Soldiers began to use uniforms that blended in with their surroundings — camouflage colors like khaki and field gray.

The American "doughboy" on the right greets the French soldier on the left during World War I.

Many countries were involved in the fighting in World War I (1914-1918). For the first time, officers' uniforms looked almost the same as those of the ordinary soldiers. Only **emblems** and cap badges were used to tell a soldier's rank and regiment. Gas masks also became an important part of everyone's uniform.

The first uniforms for airmen appeared with the formation of the Royal Flying Corps, which had 2,000 officers and men and 110 airplanes by the end of 1916. To begin with, the airmen used to drop bombs over the sides of their planes by hand!

The "doughboy," the US infantryman of 1917, had a very high quality uniform compared with the other allies. He wore an olive green uniform, often with double seams. His campaign hat with a Montana peak was replaced by a steel helmet for trench warfare. His webbing belt carried cartridges and field dressings. In his large canvas pack, he carried his greatcoat and a blanket roll fitted on top of it. His rifle was called a Springfield.

This Australian light horseman of World War I is wearing a camouflage khaki uniform. The color blends in with the desert surroundings.

Below German soldiers of World War I. The soldiers on the right are wearing gas masks.

World War II

There was a great variety of uniforms worn in World War II. The Finnish troops traveled across the snow on skis and used reindeer to help them. They wore white clothing which was almost invisible against the snow. They often took the Russians, who were short of ski troops and proper camouflage clothing, by surprise. (At the beginning of the war, the Russians fought on the German side).

The British soldiers who fought the Germans in North Africa were called "desert rats." They wore lightweight khaki shorts and shirts suitable for hot, dry, dusty conditions. They also needed a blanket or warm greatcoat for the cold nights spent out in the desert.

The Australian troops fighting the Japanese in the New Guinea jungle in 1942 wore cool camouflage uniforms and a broad hat to protect them from the hot sun and heavy rainstorms. They had to carry all their equipment with them. So did the Japanese soldiers, who were efficient and well-trained.

These Australian jungle fighters are wearing their combat uniform during World War II.

The goggles, helmet, and life jacket worn by British airmen during World War II.

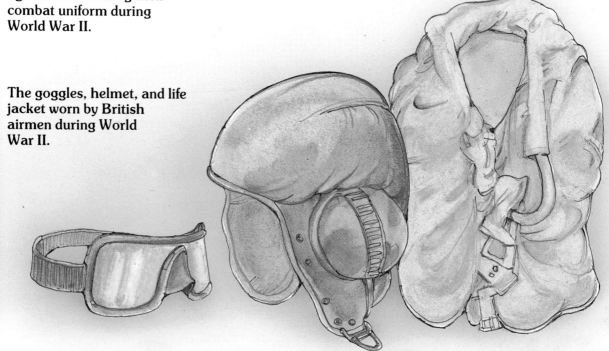

Two members of the WAAF (Women's Air Force) pictured during World War II. They are wearing peaked hats and armbands with S.P., the initials which means they are special policewomen.

During World War II, everyone had to have a gas mask. Here, a schoolteacher is showing a little boy how to put on his gas mask.

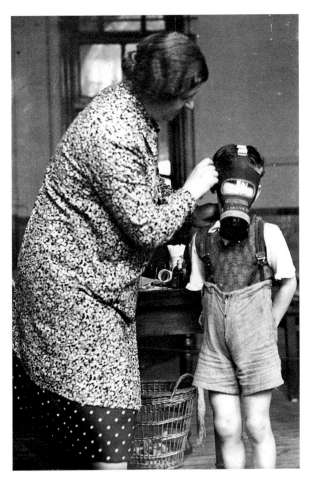

The German troops were well-equipped for street fighting in Europe. They wore helmets, strong boots for climbing through the rubble of the bombed cities, belts of cartridges, **mortars**, hand grenades, and machine guns. Their uniforms were made of tough material in drab olive green so that they could "disappear" from sight when necessary.

There were many women's uniforms used during World War II. There were ambulance or **dispatch drivers**, who wore dark jackets and slacks like the men. Women who worked in the munitions factories sometimes wore boiler suits, and British "land girls" wore uniforms suited to working in the fields. Everyone had a tin helmet as part of their uniform in case of an air raid.

Modern uniforms

In ordinary clothes, soldiers in a group would be called a crowd, not an army, because it is the uniform which makes them soldiers. Wearing a cap or helmet makes people look less at the face of an individual soldier. The person has little importance apart from his or her place as part of the whole army. The uniform tells us that the soldier takes orders from his or her superiors without question.

Chinese soldiers from the People's Liberation Army wear identical uniforms to show they have a common aim.

Gurkha officers and soldiers during a parade in Nepal.

Today, there are hundreds of different uniforms used by people in the armed forces all over the world. Each one is suited to different climates and to the different jobs that the men and women do. The Russian soldier on maneuvers in the freezing Arctic wears a very different uniform from the U.S. Navy Officer patrolling the Pacific Ocean. The Welsh Guards officer on parade wears a scarlet coat and a tall bearskin hat. He uses a camouflage uniform for his combat clothes. The many different nationalities and customs are reflected in very different uniforms. Sikh soldiers wear turbans, and Scottish soldiers wear kilts.

Each uniform needs to be tough, practical, and suited to the job done by the wearer. The British military police sometimes wear an N.B.C. (Nuclear, Biological, and Chemical) warfare suit in case of contamination in the event of a nuclear attack. They wear this on top of a full combat uniform. The N.B.C. is made of cotton **impregnated** with charcoal and chemicals which protect against nuclear fallout. They also use a **respirator** to breathe through which lasts for twenty-four hours.

Above A member of the MPLA (Popular Movement for the Liberation of Angola) photographed in combat uniform.

This soldier is testing a chemical warfare suit and respirator.

Civilian Uniforms

Everyday uniforms

The uniforms worn by certain people show others which jobs they do. Air stewards and stewardesses, hotel doormen, and some salesclerks wear uniforms so that people can recognize them if they need help. Their uniforms help them to stand out from the crowd. Uniforms identify the worker, but can also protect ordinary clothes from getting dirty or being damaged. The chef's uniform protects ordinary clothes, is clean and **hygienic** for dealing with food, and is cool to wear in a hot kitchen. His tall hat makes the chef stand out from all the other kitchen workers.

Many people wear overalls or dusters as part of their uniform, like those worn by catering and cleaning workers. This protects their ordinary clothes very efficiently. Overalls are rarely made from materials like cotton or linen which are hard to clean, but are usually made from a synthetic fiber that can be easily cleaned and does not need to be ironed.

Some workers need heavy-duty protection against the rough work that they do. Construction workers often wear helmets and a boiler suit made out of a tough material that gives protection from cuts and grazes. Uniforms also need to be good at protecting the wearer from dirt. A car mechanic's working uniform gets covered in oil and grease very quickly!

Look how spotless this chef's starched white uniform is. It is extremely important that people who work in restaurants look clean and hygienic.

Bus drivers and engineers in cold countries often have uniforms which are made of warm suit material. They usually wear a hat or cap of some kind, too. In hot countries, they wear loose, cotton clothes. Other uniforms which are perhaps not so obvious are those worn by business people who work in cities all over the world. They wear similar clothes to show that they belong to the same group and have the same type of jobs.

Above **This Japanese car mechanic is wearing a stylish blue uniform, with his company logo on the hat and overalls.**

People who drive buses in New Zealand wear stylish, efficient uniforms that show which bus company they work for. They also give a good impression to people traveling on the bus.

Uniforms which show rank and importance

A traffic warden and a police or fire officer can be recognized immediately by their uniforms. It is very important that people can see that they are performing their special duties. We might not take any notice of police officers in their ordinary clothes. (Which is just what plainclothes police officers, like detectives, want!) Riot policemen and women wear helmets and carry shields to protect themselves from stones and other missiles thrown by an angry crowd. Because their uniform looks frightening, it can sometimes be a **deterrent** to the rioters.

Above **British fire officers' uniforms are brightly colored, which makes them easily recognizable in an emergency.**

These riot police officers are lined up in case of trouble at a student demonstration in Tokyo. They are wearing crash helmets in case they are hit by stones, thick gloves, and bulletproof jackets under their uniforms.

Sometimes, a uniform is used to show a person's rank or importance. Some clothes are like uniforms because they show the rank of the person wearing them. In Egypt, long ago, only important people wore white. The queen wore a crown and a white dress to show her rank and power. Chiefs of some North American Indian tribes wore a headdress of eagle's feathers which made them stand out from the other Indians, showing that they were high-ranking and powerful.

Officers in the armed services wear grander uniforms than soldiers in the lower ranks. Kings and queens wear royal costumes for state occasions. Churchmen and women wear ceremonial robes. In Britain, mayors and mayoresses wear heavy chains of office, and U.S. sheriffs wear badges. Many of these historical uniforms have been worn for many centuries, and they are still worn today to help make us respect old customs and traditions.

Above **The Lord Mayor of London wears an ornate chain of office to show her importance.**

This Sioux chief's magnificent headdress shows he is high-ranking and important.

Uniforms in education

Can you think of any reasons why school children wear uniforms? They certainly make them stand out in a crowded street. By wearing school uniforms, ordinary clothes wear out less quickly. School uniforms often have badges or special belts and ribbons which show rank or importance. Often, the school has a badge of its own which is worn on the blazer pocket. This gives a sense of belonging to the school group. Most schoolchildren do not wear uniforms today. Some schools prefer for children to wear what they please, as they believe children should be encouraged to look and act as individuals.

Students who do not have to wear uniforms can still often buy a school sweater or scarf. Uniforms are used for special occasions, such as when people receive their degrees at graduation ceremonies. Then, the caps and gowns that were worn in the past by tutors and academics are put on. Only people who have earned a degree are allowed to wear these clothes, which make them feel special and important.

These Japanese children sitting down to have lunch, wear identical uniforms to show they are members of the same school.

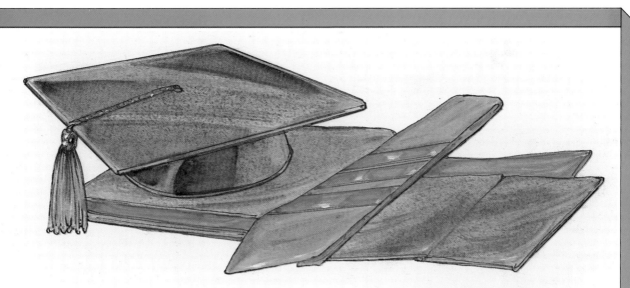

Below Students dressed in caps and gowns at a graduation ceremony in Kenya.

Above The mortarboard (hat), gown, and college tie worn by many students at graduation ceremonies.

Uniforms in religion

Special clothes are worn by religious leaders all over the world. A Roman Catholic priest wears a long gown called a cassock over which he wears rich, ornate vestments. Anglican clergy wear a stiff, white clerical collar which is sometimes called a "dog collar."

Many people wear special clothes to show which religion they follow. Women in some Moslem countries are expected to wear long black robes which completely cover their bodies, and masks which only show their eyes. Some jewish men wear a small skullcap on their heads called a yarmulkah. Christian monks and nuns wear simple clothes to show that they have given up their ordinary lives to serve God and their fellow human beings. Buddhist monks dress humbly, too, wearing plain **saffron** or red robes. Members of the Amish sect wear very plain uniforms: black suits and wide-brimmed hats and long dresses and bonnets.

Uniforms are worn by ordinary people at special ceremonies like weddings, christenings, and funerals. In Europe, North America, and Australia, white is usually worn for weddings and baptisms, and church choirs wear gowns and starched collars. Black clothes are usually worn for funerals in Europe, but in China, white is worn. Sometimes, special uniforms are worn for praying. Jews wear a "praying shawl." In some parts of Africa, people put on masks and paint themselves for religious ceremonies. The purpose of these special clothes is to direct people's minds to what they are doing. It also tells other people that the religious ceremony is important to those taking part.

Some women who follow the Islamic religion wear long robes covering their bodies. This is known as purdah.

Above Young Buddhist monks wear saffron robes to show that they belong to the Theravada sect of Buddhism.

This Roman Catholic cardinal (one of the advisors to the Pope) is wearing traditional red and black robes.

Uniforms in medicine

People who performed operations and looked after the sick or injured used to wear ordinary clothes. For hundreds of years, "quack" doctors posed as experts in medicine. They used to sell "miracle cures," which were often quite dangerous. As soon as discoveries were made about the use of **antiseptics**, how diseases spread, and the importance of cleanliness and hygiene, uniforms became the standard dress of those people working in medicine

You would not enjoy having your teeth pulled out by this eighteenth-century "quack" doctor. "Quack" doctors were not qualified professionals and wore no uniforms.

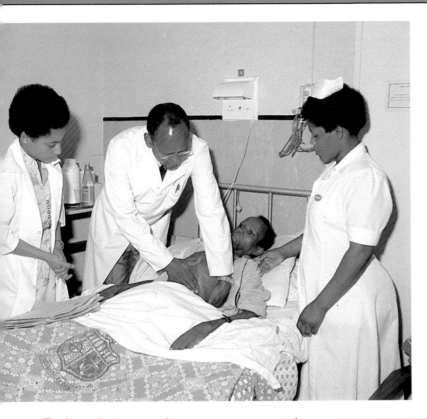

This doctor and his student examining the patient have different uniforms from the nurse. Both, however, are clean, white, and efficient and give a hygienic impression

Below This anesthetist is responsible for keeping a patient unconscious during an operation. He is wearing a surgical mask to prevent germs from spreading.

Today, doctors and nurses wear special uniforms that protect the patient from infection and protect their own clothes. The doctor's white coat is a sign of importance and cleanliness to patients and hospital workers. The coat does not rely on badges or colorful ornaments to suggest this importance. The **stethoscope** that doctors carry could be considered part of the uniform.

The uniforms worn by those who work in operating rooms have to be strictly hygienic. Everyone wears a mask, rubber gloves over their scrubbed clean hands, a hat, and a **sterile** gown. Even when students watch an operation, they have to wear masks and gowns.

Nurses' uniforms are practical and cool to wear. They need comfortable, sensible shoes for their many different duties. The colored bands on nurses' hats or the belts worn as part of their uniform can show their various ranks. Senior nurses wear different uniforms from ordinary nurses, which make them stand apart.

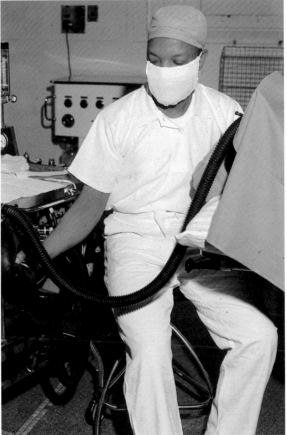

Uniforms in sports

At one time, there were no uniforms or even special sports clothes. When soccer was first played, players turned out in whatever they happened to be wearing at the time. The first "uniforms" look comical to modern eyes. What looked like full-length underwear topped by a nightcap was standard wear. Women played tennis in long, uncomfortable dresses.

This picture shows a soccer match between England and Scotland in 1875. It is interesting to see how different the uniforms are to those worn today.

Sporting people are testing their energy, strength, skill and speed. Special clothes can help them perform well. Gymnasts' and swimmers' uniforms give them as much complete freedom of movement as possible. Soccer players need special shoes to stop them from slipping, and sprinters need shoes with sharp spikes in the sole.

Players in contact sports often need protection. Boxers need padded gloves. Football players have to wear helmets and pad their bodies and legs. In motor racing or cycling, people need protection against high speed crashes, collisions, and fire. They wear uniforms which include helmets and flame-proof clothes. The uniforms of ice hockey players include a lot of thick body-padding to protect them against collisions with other players and falls on the ice.

Team colors are a kind of uniform. A football player needs to be able to tell at a glance which team a player is on. Often, a number is part of a uniform to help identify a player's position on the field. Sporting uniforms can be very different, even when they are worn by participants in the same sport. The uniforms of football players and the cheerleaders on the sideline are different!

The one-piece cap and swimsuit worn by the Swedish women's relay team at the 1984 Olympic Games in Los Angeles fitted like skin.

Unusual Uniforms

Sometimes, young people in groups wear the same daring or rebellious clothes. It is almost like wearing a uniform. In the 1950s, Teddy boys in Britain started to dress differently from their parents. They wore dark, narrow Teddy suits and crepe-soled shoes as a sign of their youth and toughness. These clothes became fashionable for many people. Punk fashion and its bright, daring hairstyles and clothes started off in the same way; so did the mod, rocker, hippie, and skinhead fashions.

There was a time when the standard uniform for many young people was a pair of blue jeans. Wearing the same style of clothes is a way of saying that the wearers think the same things about life. Perhaps you think that this is true of some groups of the older generation, who also tend to wear the same kind of clothes.

These punks in London share the same ideas about fashion.

Terrorists show that they think the same things about life by wearing the same uniforms. Often, they want to remain unrecognized, so they cover up their faces. The Klu Klux Klan use frightening tall, white, pointed masks with slits for the eyes and mouths as part of their uniform.

In the world of entertainment, there are some very unusual uniforms. The chorus in some operas wear the same uniforms or costumes. Chorus ballerinas often wear short, frilly "tutus" of the same color. Some pop groups look impressive when they wear identical clothes and dance to the same routine. Orchestras and their conductors usually wear special clothes for performances. The men wear formal black suits, and the women wear black skirts and blouses or black dresses.

Traditional costumes are worn with pride all over the world and could be said to be a kind of uniform. They are often richly colored and beautifully decorated.

Above During "carnival," the annual Mardi Gras festival held in Rio de Janeiro in Brazil, people dress up in all sorts of magnificent colorful costumes.

Today, many pop stars such as the Beastie Boys dress in styles that are easy for their fans to copy. This "uniform" of jeans, tee shirts, and baseball caps can easily be identified by fellow fans.

Glossary

Agile   Lively, active, and quick in movement.

Antiseptic   A liquid, cream, or spray which stops infection.

Armor   A protective metal or leather covering worn in fighting.

Braid   Narrow ornamental tape of woven or plaited material.

Cartridge   A metal case containing an explosive charge or sometimes a bullet.

Conical   Cone-shaped.

Deterrent   Something which stops or prevents people from doing something.

Dispatch rider   A motorcyclist who carries messages.

Greatcoat   A heavy overcoat worn by members of the armed forces.

Greave   A piece of armor worn to protect the shin.

Hauberk   A long sleeveless coat of armor.

Hygienic   Clean and healthy.

Impregnated   Saturated or soaked.

Khaki   A dull, light greenish-brown color, used especially for soldiers' uniforms.

Middle Ages   The period of time between the fall of the Roman Empire and the Italian Renaissance, 500-1500 A.D.

Mortar   A small cannon that fires shells.

Plume   Feathers worn as ornament in a headband or on a hat.

Respirator   Device worn over the nose and mouth to prevent the wearer from breathing in poisonous fumes.

Saber   A heavy, slightly curved, one-edged sword.

Saffron   An orange-yellow color.

Shako   A tall, cylindrical hat with a plume and sometimes a peak.

Sterile   Free from germs.

Stethoscope   An instrument for listening to the sounds made inside the body.

Books to Read

If you would like to find out more about uniforms, you may like to read the following books.

Clothes by Peter Curry (Price Stern, 1984).

Costumes and Clothes by Jean Cooke (Franklin Watts, 1987).

A Day in the Life of a Firefighter (cassettes available) (Troll Associates, 1981).

Indian Costumes by Robert Hofside (William Morrow, 1986).

The Medieval Knight by Martin Windrow (Franklin Watts, 1986).

Motorcycle on Patrol: The Story of a Highway Office (Ticknor & Fields, 1986).

New Clothes: What People Wore from Cavemen to Astronauts by Lisl Weil (Macmillan, 1987).

The World War I Tommy by Martin Windrow (Franklin Watts, 1986).

The World War II G.I. by Martin Windrow (Franklin Watts, 1986).

Index

Acknowledgements

The publishers would like to thank the following for providing the pictures for this book: All-sport 5 (top), 27; BBC Hulton 13 (bottom); Mary Evans Picture Library 7 (top); Format Photographers 18 (top), 19 (top), 25 (bottom); The Hutchison Library 15 (top), 22, 23 (bottom); Paul Jordan 6 (right), 11 (bottom), 15 (bottom); Peter Newark's Western Americana 8 (top), 9, 10, 11 (top), 12 (top), 19 (bottom); Julia Osorno 6 (left), 8 (bottom), 12 (bottom), 21 (top); David Redfern 29; South American Pictures 29; Topham Picture Library 13 (top); Wayland Picture Library 5 (bottom), 7 (bottom), 14 (top), 17, 21 (bottom), 24, 25 (top); ZEFA 4, 14 (bottom), 16, 18 (bottom), 20, 23 (top), 28.